Gg
Hh
Ii
Jj
Kk
Ll
Mm
Uu
Vv
Ww
Xx
Yy
Zz

Dear Parent,

The My First Steps to Reading® *series is based on a teaching activity that helps children learn to recognize letters and their sounds. The use of predictable language patterns and repetition of familiar words will also help your child build a basic sight vocabulary. Your child will enjoy watching the characters in the books place imaginative objects in "letter boxes." You and your child can even create and fill your own letter box, using stuffed animals, cut-out pictures, or other objects beginning with the same letter. The things you can do together are limited only by your imagination. Learning letters will be fun—the first important step on the road to reading.*

The Editors

 Published by Scholastic Inc., 90 Old Sherman Turnpike, Danbury, Connecticut 06810, by arrangement with The Child's World, Inc.
Scholastic offers a varied selection of children's book racks and tote bags. For details about ordering, please write to: Scholastic At Home, 90 Old Sherman Turnpike, Danbury, CT 06810, Attention: Premium Department

Originally published as *My "v" Sound Box* by The Child's World, Inc.

My First Steps to Reading is a registered trademark of Grolier Publishing Co. Inc.
SCHOLASTIC and associated logos are trademarks and/or registered trademarks of Scholastic Inc.

ISBN 0-7172-6521-8

Printed in the U.S.A.

My "v" Book

written by Jane Belk Moncure
illustrated by Colin King

Little V had a box.

“I will find things that begin with my ‘v’ sound,” she said.

“I will put them into my sound box.”

Little v found violets,

all kinds of very pretty violets.

She put some violets into a vase.

Then she put the vase with the violets

into her box.

Next, Little V found

a piece of velvet,

very pretty velvet.

She made a velvet vest.

She put it on and pinned
a velvet bow on it.

She put velvet all around her box.
"What a very pretty box," she said.

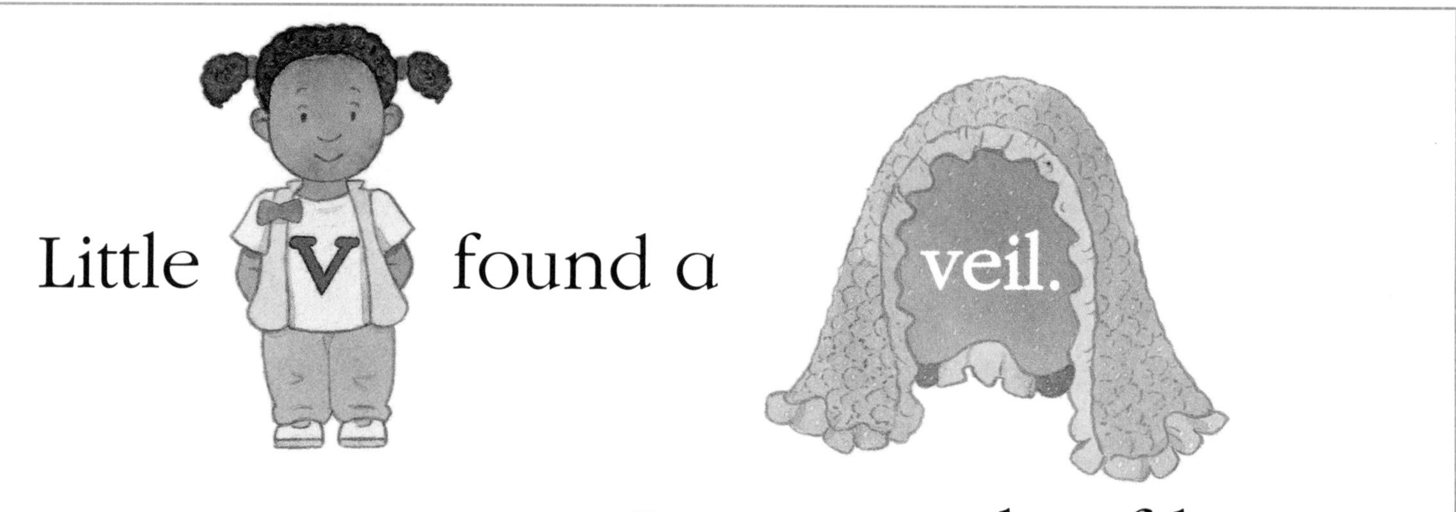

Little V found a veil.

It was made of lace.

"Oh," she said.
"I can make something
with my violets and velvet

and lace veil."

Do you know what Little V made?

She made valentines,

very nice valentines.

Then she found a valentine verse.

She wrote the verse on her valentines.

Then she filled her box with valentines. She pasted valentines all around the box.

But some valentines fell out.

"What shall I do with all these valentines?" she asked.

"I will send the valentines to my friends."

Then Little V had a very good idea.

She wrote another verse on each valentine:

She put the valentines into envelopes.
She put her friends' names and
addresses on the envelopes.
There were very many.

Little V got into her van
and drove to the mailbox.

When Little got back home, she

got out the vacuum.

She used the vacuum to clean up the scraps of velvet and valentines.

On Valentine's Day,
her friends came
to her party.
Each one brought
valentines.

Little  and her friends made

valentine hats.

They put on their valentine hats
and played some games.

Then they opened the valentines.

What fun they had at . . .

the Valentine's Day party!

Can you read these words
with Little V ?
vegetables
volleyball
violin
vine

vitamins
volcano
vampire
vinegar
valley

Aa Bb Cc Dd Ee Ff

Nn Oo Pp Qq Rr Ss Tt

My First Steps to READING®